I don't know why she swallowed a fly. Perhaps she'll die.

There was an old lady who swallowed a spider,
that wriggled and wriggled and jiggled inside her.

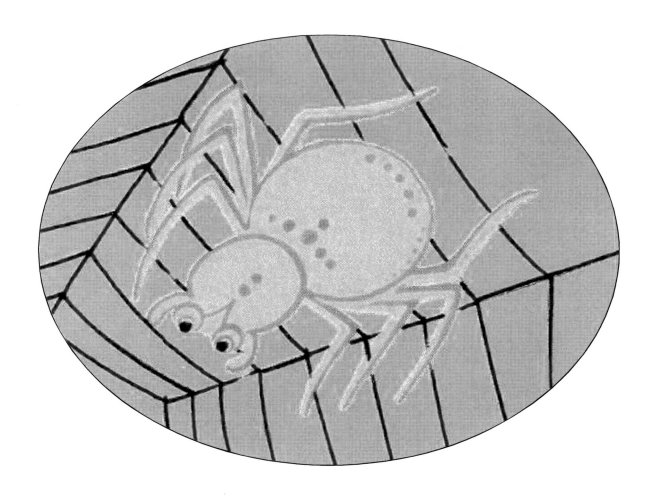

She swallowed the spider to catch the fly.

I don't know why she swallowed a fly. Perhaps she'll die.

There was an old lady who swallowed a bird. How absurd, to swallow a bird!

She swallowed the bird to catch the spider.

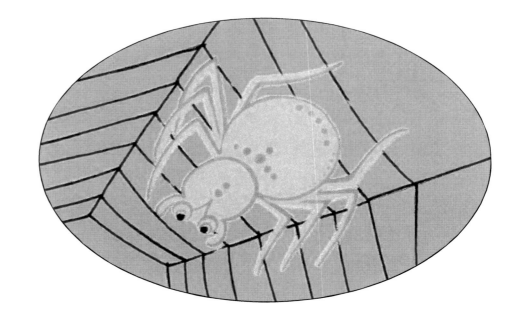

She swallowed the spider to catch the fly.

I don't know why she swallowed a fly. Perhaps she'll die.

There was an old lady who swallowed a cat.
Well, fancy that, she swallowed a cat!

She swallowed the cat to catch the bird.

She swallowed the bird to catch the spider.

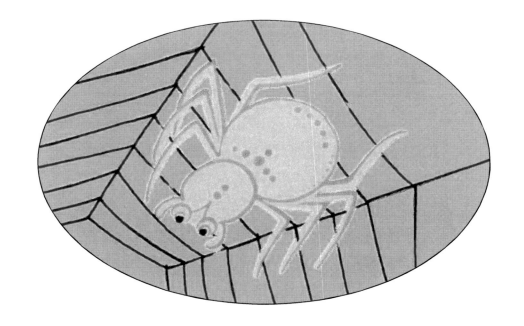

She swallowed the spider to catch the fly.

I don't know why she swallowed a fly. Perhaps she'll die.

There was an old lady who swallowed a dog.
What a hog, to swallow a dog!

She swallowed the dog to catch the cat.

She swallowed the cat to catch the bird.

She swallowed the bird to catch the spider.

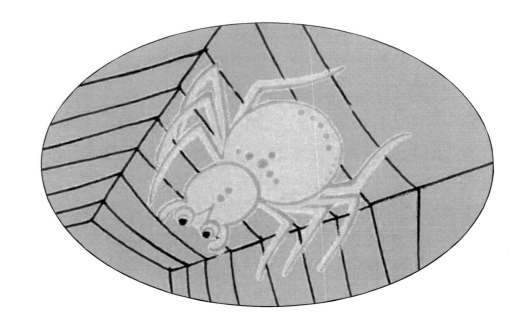

She swallowed the spider to catch the fly.

I don't know why she swallowed a fly. Perhaps she'll die.

There was an old lady who swallowed a cow. I don't know how she swallowed a cow!

She swallowed the cow to catch the dog.

She swallowed the dog to catch the cat.

She swallowed the cat to catch the bird.

She swallowed the bird to catch the spider.

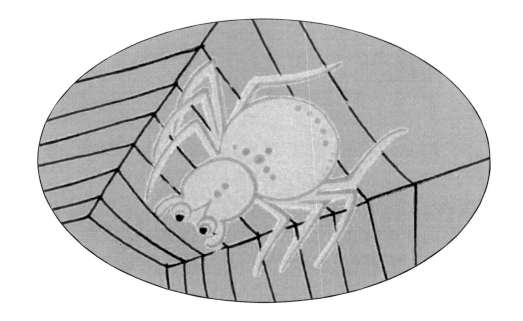

She swallowed the spider to catch the fly.

I don't know why
she swallowed a fly.
Perhaps she'll die.

There was an old lady who swallowed a horse.

She's dead
of course.

THE END

**There was an old lady
who swallowed a fly
Copyright © M. Twinn 1973
Illustrated by Pam Adams
Published in 2010/1 by
Child's Play (International) Ltd
Ashworth Road Swindon UK
Published in 2012 by Access2Books
www.access2books.org
ISBN 978-1-909225-31-2**